STECK-VAUGHN

LEVEL

A

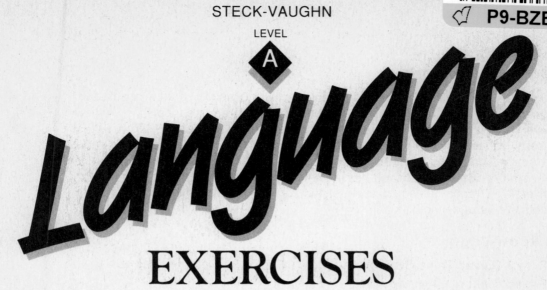

Language

EXERCISES

Betty Jones
Saranna Moeller
Cynthia T. Strauch

STECK-VAUGHN
COMPANY
A subsidiary of National Education Corporation

About the Authors

Saranna S. Moeller has been a teacher in the elementary grades for over twenty-five years. Moeller received her bachelor's degree in education from the University of Houston. She now operates the Refugio Learning Center in Texas.

Betty Jones earned her master's degree in education from Prairie View A & M University. Jones has been an elementary teacher for over twenty-five years.

Cynthia T. Strauch attained her master's degree in education at Texas A & I University. Strauch is also an experienced elementary school teacher, with over sixteen years of service.

Acknowledgments

Senior Editor: Diane Sharpe

Project Editor: Stephanie Muller

Product Development: The Wheetley Company, Inc.

Cover Design: Sue Heatly Design

Illustrations: Michael Krone

Photography: p. 18 Cindi Ellis; p. 35 Ricardo Chapa; p. 37 Cindi Ellis

Macmillan Publishing Company: Pronunciation Key, reprinted with permission of the publisher, from *Macmillan School Dictionary 1.* Copyright © 1990 Macmillan Publishing Company, a division of Macmillan, Inc.

LANGUAGE EXERCISES Series:

Level A/Pink	Level D/Gray	Level G/Gold
Level B/Orange	Level E/Red	Level H/Green
Level C/Violet	Level F/Blue	Review/Yellow

ISBN 0-8114-4190-3

6 7 8 9 PO 98 97 96 95 94

Table of Contents

UNIT 1 Readiness/Study Skills

1 ▪ Following Directions 1
2 ▪ More About Following Directions 2
3 ▪ Finding the One That Is the Same 3
4 ▪ Finding the One That Is Different 4
5 ▪ Putting Things in Groups 5
6 ▪ Listening to a Story 6
7 ▪ Listening and Remembering 7
8 ▪ Listening and Thinking 8
9 ▪ Writing Capital Letters 9
10 ▪ Writing Small Letters 10
11 ▪ Comparing Letters 11
12 ▪ Connecting Letters in ABC Order 12
13 ▪ Putting Words in ABC Order 13
Review...........................14
Using What You've Learned...........15

UNIT 2 Vocabulary

14 ▪ Listening to Sounds................17
15 ▪ Listening to Rhyming Words.......18
16 ▪ Listening to More Rhyming Words 19
17 ▪ Choosing Words with Like Meanings 20
18 ▪ Writing Words with Like Meanings 21
19 ▪ Choosing Words with Opposite Meanings 22
20 ▪ Writing Words with Opposite Meanings 23
21 ▪ Choosing the Right Meaning.......24
22 ▪ Writing Words That Sound Alike 25
Review...........................26
Using What You've Learned...........27

UNIT 3 Sentences

23 ▪ Sentences 29
24 ▪ Word Order in Sentences 30
25 ▪ More Word Order in Sentences 31
26 ▪ Sentences That Tell 32
27 ▪ Sentences That Ask...............33
28 ▪ Telling or Asking Sentences 34
29 ▪ Sentence Parts That Name 35
30 ▪ Sentence Parts That Show Action 36
31 ▪ Combining Sentence Parts........37
Review...........................38
Using What You've Learned...........39

UNIT 4 Grammar and Usage

32 ▪ Naming Words 41
33 ▪ Two Kinds of Naming Words 42
34 ▪ More Naming Words 43
35 ▪ One and More Than One 44
36 ▪ Action Words 45
37 ▪ Using Action Words...............46
38 ▪ Action Words with One or More ...47
39 ▪ Action Words for Today 48
40 ▪ Action Words for Yesterday........49
41 ▪ Using *Is* or *Are* 50
42 ▪ Using *Was* or *Were*.............51
43 ▪ Using *See, Come,* and *Run*........52
44 ▪ Using *She* and *He* 53
45 ▪ Using *We* and *They* 54
46 ▪ Using *I*........................55
47 ▪ Using *An* 56
48 ▪ Using *A* or *An* 57
49 ▪ Using Describing Words 58
50 ▪ Using More Describing Words 59
Review...........................60
Using What You've Learned...........61

UNIT 5 Capitalization and Punctuation

51 ▪ Beginning a Sentence..............63
52 ▪ Writing Names of People..........64
53 ▪ Writing Names of Pets............65
54 ▪ Writing Names of Days...........66
55 ▪ Writing Names of Months........67
56 ▪ Writing Names of Places.........68
57 ▪ Writing *I*.........................69
58 ▪ Ending a Telling Sentence........70
59 ▪ Ending an Asking Sentence.......71
60 ▪ Ending Sentences.................72
61 ▪ Writing Dates.....................73
Review...................................74
Using What You've Learned............75

UNIT 6 Composition

62 ▪ Writing Sentences with Naming
   Words..............................77
63 ▪ Writing Sentences with Action
   Words..............................78
64 ▪ Writing Sentences.................79
65 ▪ Writing More Sentences...........80
66 ▪ A Thank-You Letter...............81
67 ▪ Writing a Thank-You Letter.......82
68 ▪ Writing a Poem...................83
Review...................................84
Using What You've Learned............85

Final Reviews

Unit 1......................................87
Unit 2......................................88
Unit 3......................................89
Unit 4......................................90
Unit 5......................................91
Unit 6......................................92

Index....................Inside Back Cover

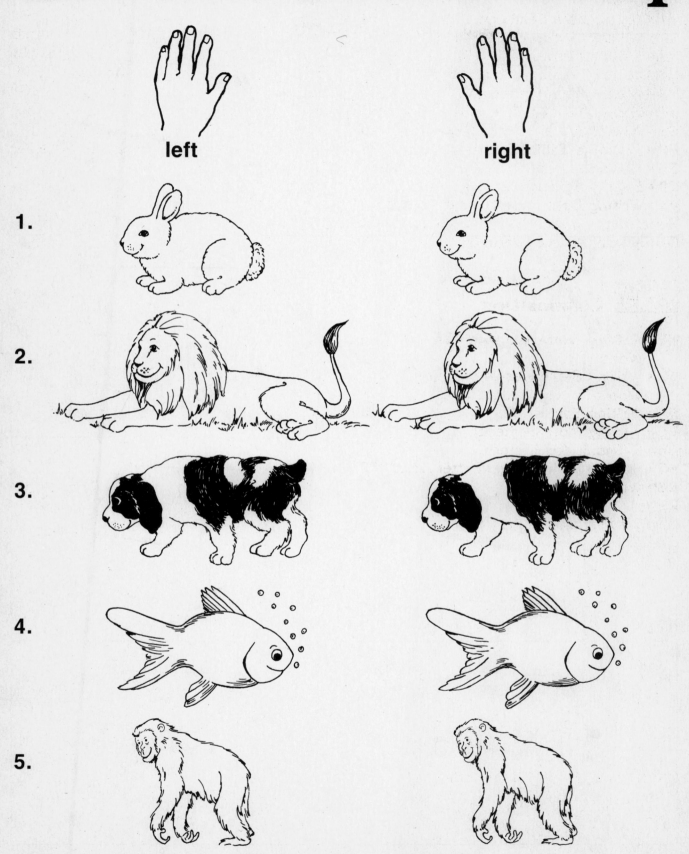

left   right

1.

2.

3.

4.

5.

Unit 1, Readiness/Study Skills. Tell students to follow the directions as you tell them which picture to circle in each row. Row 1—the bunny on the left; Row 2—the lion on the right; Row 3—the puppy on the left; Row 4—the fish on the left; Row 5—the monkey on the right.

1

More About Following Directions

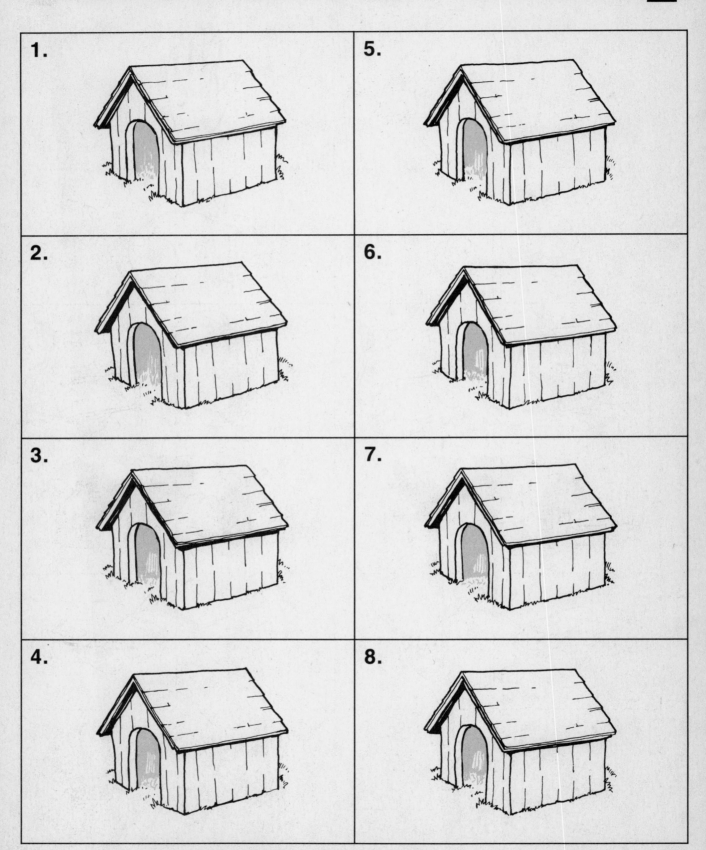

1.

2.

3.

4.

5.

6.

7.

8.

Unit 1, Readiness/Study Skills. Have students mark an *X* in the following locations: Box 1—on the doghouse; Box 2—above it; Box 3—below it; Box 4—to the right of it; Box 5—to the left of it; Box 6—inside the doorway; Box 7—on the roof. Have students draw a circle around the doghouse in Box 8.

Finding the One That Is the Same

1.

2.

3.

4.

5.

6.

Unit 1, Readiness/Study Skills. Have students look at the first picture in each row. Tell students to find another picture in the row that is exactly the same and to circle it.

4

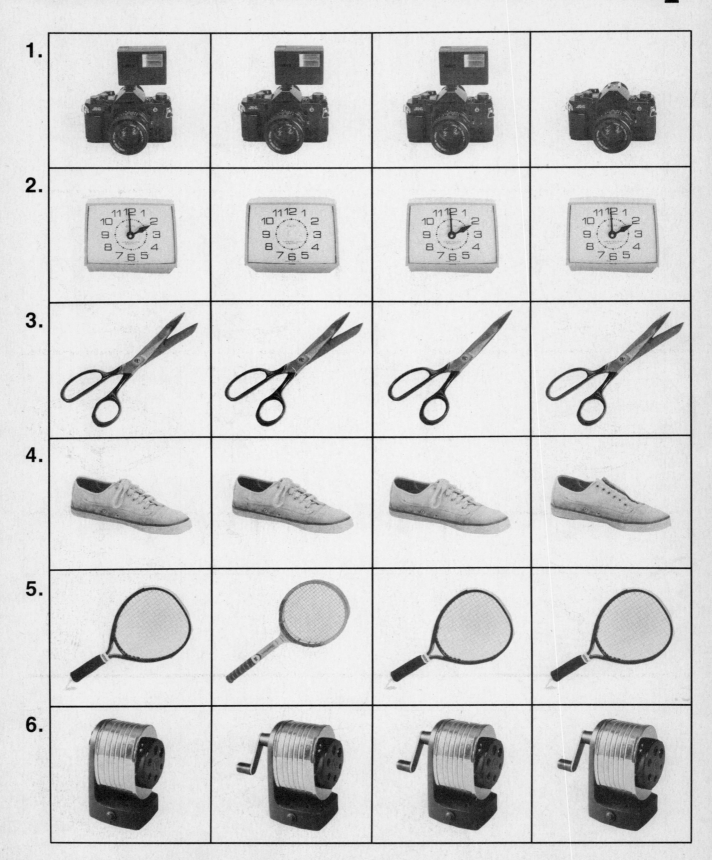

Unit 1, Readiness/Study Skills. Have students look at the pictures in each row, decide which one is different, and circle the different one.

Putting Things in Groups

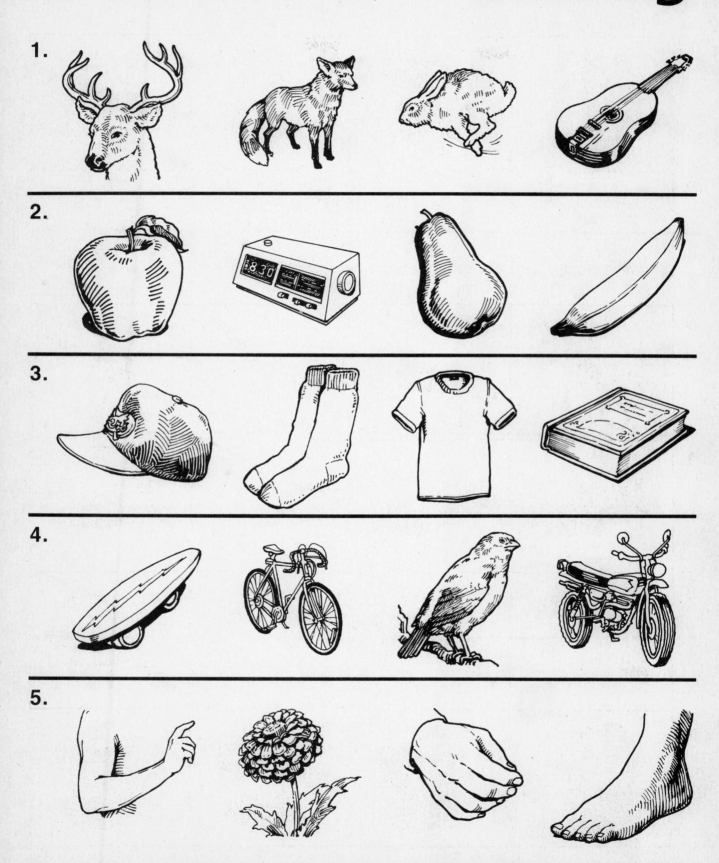

1.

2.

3.

4.

5.

Unit 1, Readiness/Study Skills.   Have one student name the objects in each row. Then have students circle the three objects in each row that are alike in some way.

1.

2.

3.

4.

Unit 1, Readiness/Study Skills.   Have students listen to the story (which appears in the *Teacher's Guide*). Read the following questions and have students circle the picture that answers the question. Row 1: What did Mom do? Row 2: What did Rosemary do? Row 3: What did Dad do? Row 4: What did Rudy do?

1.

2.

Unit 1, Readiness/Study Skills.   Have students listen as you read the first story (which appears in the *Teacher's Guide*). Then tell them to look at the picture of Beth and Bill, and to draw a line from the dot to what they did first, next, and last. Repeat the procedure with the second story.

7

1.

2.

3.

4.

5.

6.

7.

8.

Unit 1, Readiness/Study Skills.   Have students listen carefully as you read the first story (which appears in the *Teacher's Guide*). Then have students mark an *X* on the picture that answers the question at the end of the story. Follow the same procedure with each story.

Writing Capital Letters

9

A B C D E F G

H I J K L M N

O P Q R S T

U V W X Y Z

Unit 1, Readiness/Study Skills. Have students pronounce the letter names in order in unison. Then have them write the capital letters on the lines.

a b c d e f g h i

j k l m n o p q r

s t u v w x y z

I can write.

Unit 1, Readiness/Study Skills. Have students pronounce the letter names in order in unison. Then have them write the small letters and the sentence on the lines.

1. 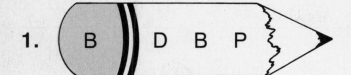 B   D   B   P

4.  C   C   G   O

2. I   T   I   L

5.  N   M   N   W

3.  O   O   Q   C

6. P   R   B   P

1. b   k   d   b   p

4. g   y   g   a   j

2. t   f   t   h   r

5.  m   s   w   n   m

3.  v   w   u   v   z

6.  f   h   t   f   k

Unit 1, Readiness/Study Skills. In the top exercise, have students name the capital letter in the eraser and circle the other letter in the pencil that is exactly like the first. Follow the same procedure with the small letters at the bottom of the page.

A B C D E F G H I J K L M N O P Q R S T U V W X Y Z

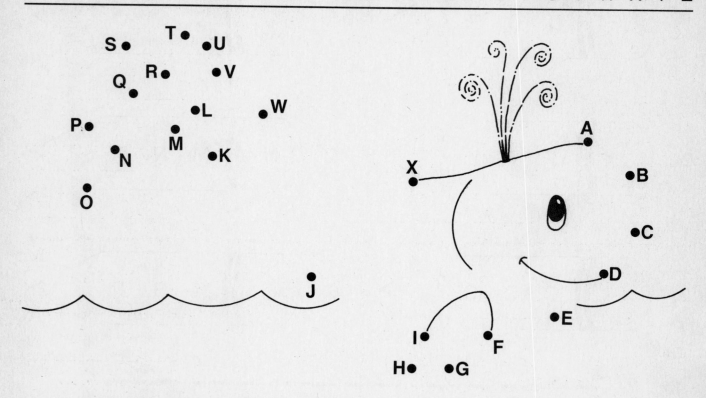

a b c d e f g h i j k l m n o p q r s t u v w x y z

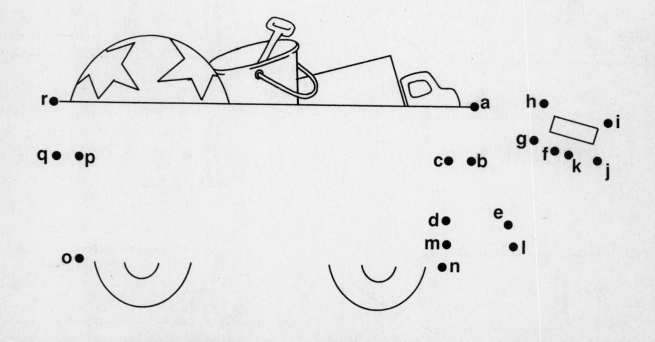

Unit 1, Readiness/Study Skills. Have students read the capital letters across the top of the page. Then have them complete the dot-to-dot picture. Follow the same procedure with the small letters at the bottom of the page.

1. a b c d e f

cat `bird`

bird _____

dog _____

4. e f g h i j

give _____

help _____

find _____

2. i j k l m n

know _____

me _____

like _____

5. l m n o p q

on _____

left _____

near _____

3. q r s t u v w x

we _____

she _____

they _____

6. m n o p q r s

red _____

one _____

name _____

Unit 1, Readiness/Study Skills.   Have students look at the first three words and the underlined letters. Ask students which of these letters comes first in the alphabet. Have them trace over *bird*. Have students determine which words come next and last and write those words. Repeat the procedure for the other groups.

13

1.

2.

---

1. M N M W   **3.** Q O Q Q

2. B C D E   **4.** g h i j

---

1. C D ____   **5.** G H ____   **9.** M N ____

2. Q R ____   **6.** U V ____   **10.** X Y ____

3. a ____ c   **7.** g ____ i   **11.** l ____ n

4. s ____ u   **8.** v ____ x   **12.** x ____ z

house

farmer

pigs

dog

barn

child

chickens

cow

Unit 1, Readiness/Study Skills.   Have students look at the objects in the picture. Read directions (which appear in the *Teacher's Guide*), and have students follow the directions.

1. A _____

2. M _____

3. G _____

4. D _____

5. P _____

6. R _____

7. F _____

8. V _____

9. Y _____

---

1. _____ b

2. _____ h

3. _____ i

4. _____ e

5. _____ n

6. _____ p

7. _____ g

8. _____ q

9. _____ k

---

1. Pat _____

Ana _____

Tom _____

2. Lin _____

Raul _____

Ella _____

Unit 1, Readiness/Study Skills. Have students point to the capital letters at the top of the page. Tell them to write the small letter that matches each capital letter. Next have students write the capital letter that matches each small letter. Then have students put each list of names in alphabetical order.

1.

5.

2.

6.

3.

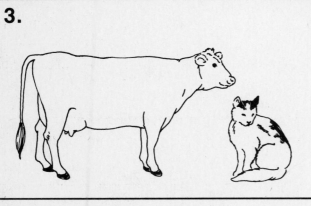

7.

4.

8.

Unit 2, Vocabulary. Have students name the pictures in each box. Then have students listen to the sounds you say and circle the animal in each box that makes that sound. Box 1: moo; Box 2: quack; Box 3: meow; Box 4: woof; Box 5: buzz; Box 6: baa; Box 7: neigh; Box 8: cheep.

1.

2.

3.

4.

5.

6.

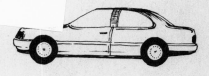

20,21

Unit 2, Vocabulary. Have students say the name of each picture in the first column and draw a line from it to the picture in rhe second column that ends with the same sound.

1. It is lots of **fun**

_____

To play in the _____. (sand, sun)

2. I can run and **hide**

_____

And go down the _____. (slide, sled)

3. Our little gray **cat**

_____

Lay on a soft _____. (mop, mat)

4. The black-and-white **bug**

_____

Went under the _____. (rug, rag)

5. A big green **frog**

_____

Sat on a _____. (log, lap)

6. The frog went **hop**

_____

Then jumped on a _____. (map, mop)

Unit 2, Vocabulary. Read each rhyme and the two word choices together. Then have students decide which word at the right rhymes with the word in dark print. Have students write the rhyming word on the lines.

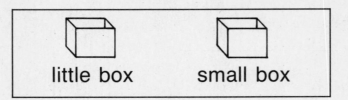

little box   small box

1. little   big   small

2. one   start   begin

3. stop   start   finish

4. sound   give   noise

5. high   down   tall

6. look   see   book

7. large   big   little

8. up   below   under

9. all   every   one

10. happy   sad   glad

---

1. My book is on the <u>little</u> table. (small, big)

2. It is a <u>large</u> book. (red, big)

3. It is about a <u>rabbit</u>. (dog, bunny)

4. My papers are <u>under</u> the book. (on, below)

5. You can <u>print</u> in my book. (see, write)

6. Now you can <u>stop</u> looking at it. (finish, be)

7. I will <u>start</u> reading my book. (be, begin)

8. I won't make a <u>sound</u>. (noise, picture)

9. Will you <u>go</u> now? (leave, stay)

10. I will be <u>glad</u> to go, too. (sad, happy)

Unit 2, Vocabulary.   Tell students that the words in the box mean almost the same. Read each group of words together, and have students circle the two words that mean almost the same. Then read the sentences together, and have students circle the word that means almost the same as the underlined word.

1. I look in the box. I see a toy bird.

_____   _____
- - - - - - - - - - - - - - - - -   - - - - - - - - - - - - - - - - -
_____   _____

2. My toy bird is little. The toy box is small.

_____   _____
- - - - - - - - - - - - - - - - -   - - - - - - - - - - - - - - - - -
_____   _____

3. The toy bird starts to sing. The music begins.

_____   _____
- - - - - - - - - - - - - - - - -   - - - - - - - - - - - - - - - - -
_____   _____

4. I place it on the table. I put the toy bird away.

_____   _____
- - - - - - - - - - - - - - - - -   - - - - - - - - - - - - - - - - -
_____   _____

1. Chan is a little cat. He is small.

_____   _____
- - - - - - - - - - - - - - - - -   - - - - - - - - - - - - - - - - -
_____   _____

2. Chan heard a sound. It was a big noise.

_____   _____
- - - - - - - - - - - - - - - - -   - - - - - - - - - - - - - - - - -
_____   _____

3. The cat ran under a tree. He was below a nest.

_____   _____
- - - - - - - - - - - - - - - - -   - - - - - - - - - - - - - - - - -
_____   _____

4. A big bird looked down. The large bird chased Chan.

_____   _____
- - - - - - - - - - - - - - - - -   - - - - - - - - - - - - - - - - -
_____   _____

Unit 2, Vocabulary.   Read the pairs of sentences together. Have students circle a word in the second sentence that means almost the same as the underlined word in the first sentence. Have them write the two words on the lines.

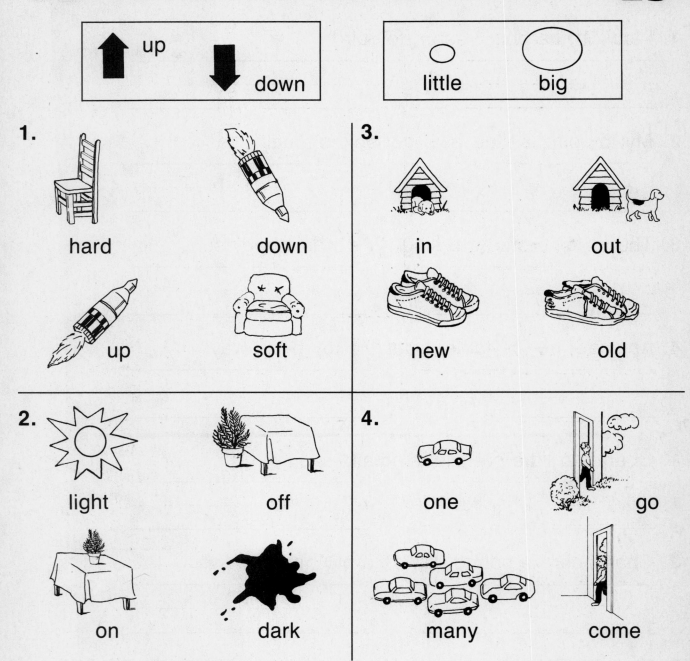

1. Peter went <u>up</u> the stairs. (down, out)

2. He sat on his <u>soft</u> bed. (new, hard)

3. It got <u>dark</u> outside. (light, cold)

4. He turned <u>on</u> the lamp. (red, off)

1. I am <u>little</u>, and my sister is ___.

_____ _____

------------------------ ------------------------

_____ _____

2. She has <u>dark</u> hair, and I have ___ hair.

_____ _____

------------------------ ------------------------

_____ _____

3. When I go <u>out</u>, she comes ___.

_____ _____

------------------------ ------------------------

_____ _____

4. Her bike is <u>old</u>, but mine is ___.

_____ _____

------------------------ ------------------------

_____ _____

5. First I get <u>on</u> my bike, then I get ___.

_____ _____

------------------------ ------------------------

_____ _____

6. I go <u>up</u> the steps and ___ the slide.

_____ _____

------------------------ ------------------------

_____ _____

7. I have a <u>hard</u> apple, and she has a ___ cookie.

_____ _____

------------------------ ------------------------

_____ _____

8. We play all <u>day</u> and sleep all ___.

_____ _____

------------------------ ------------------------

_____ _____

big
down
in
light
new
night
off
soft

Unit 2, Vocabulary. Read the sentences together. Have students choose an opposite for each underlined word, then write the two opposites on the lines.

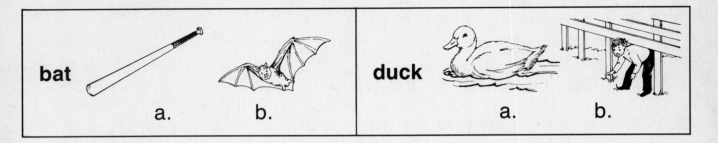

bat   a.   b.   duck   a.   b.

1. Steve hit the ball with a <u>bat</u>. ____

2. The <u>bat</u> likes the dark. ____

3. Juan plays ball with a heavy <u>bat</u>. ____

4. He wants to know how a <u>bat</u> sees at night. ____

5. I'd like a new glove and <u>bat</u>. ____

---

1. The <u>duck</u> made a loud quack. ____

2. There was a <u>duck</u> with four ducklings on the pond. ____

3. We had to <u>duck</u> under a fence. ____

4. We were asked to <u>duck</u> so they could see. ____

5. The <u>duck</u> swam in the water. ____

Unit 2, Vocabulary.   Have students look at the words at the top of the page and the pairs of pictures that illustrate the different meanings of the words. Then read each sentence together, and have students write the letter of the correct meaning in each space.

to

1. I took a ball _____ Ben.

_____

- -

_____

2. Ben went _____ the game.

_____

- -

_____

3. He wants _____ play.

_____

- -

_____

two

4. There are _____ animals.

_____

- -

_____

5. They each have _____ ears.

_____

- -

_____

1. I have (two, to) hands.

2. I use them (two, to) clap.

3. My house has (two, to) doors.

4. I open them (two, to) go outside.

5. I am going (two, to) the park.

Unit 2, Vocabulary. Review the meanings of *to* and *two*. Have students add *to* or *two* to each incomplete sentence, then write the complete sentence. Next have students circle the correct word in each sentence at the bottom of the page.

1. star   car   bat

2. log   hat   frog

3. tug   rug   big

4. boat   goat   cap

5. door   mouse   house

6. cat   hat   sit

7. ran   run   sun

8. ants   pants   tin

---

1. hard   down

2. up   new

3. old   soft

4. push   pull

5. in   dark

6. go   out

7. light   come

8. on   off

1. little   big

2. stop   end

3. large   small

4. start   see

5. sound   begin

6. look   noise

7. print   under

8. below   write

---

1. Rosa has __ books. (two, to)

2. She went __ school. (two, to)

3. She likes __ read. (two, to)

4. Her __ friends like to read. (two, to)

5. They went __ the library. (two, to)

6. They each took out __ books. (two, to)

---

26   **Unit 2, Vocabulary.**   Section 1—Have students circle the words that rhyme. Section 2—Have students draw lines to connect the words that are opposites. Section 3—Have students draw lines to connect the words that mean the same. Section 4—Have students circle *two* or *to* for each sentence.

black	two	read	boy

1. Kenji is the new _____ in class.
toy

2. He has _____ hair.
sack

3. Kenji likes to _____ books.
seed

4. He has read _____ books today.
who

two	to

1. I met _____ friends at the show.

2. We wanted _____ see something scary.

3. We bought _____ hotdogs.

4. We tried _____ find the best seats.

5. There were _____ bats in the show.

Unit 2, Vocabulary. Read the sentences at the top of the page together, and have students write the word from the box that rhymes with the word below the lines. Then have students write *two* or *to* for the sentences at the bottom of the page.

27

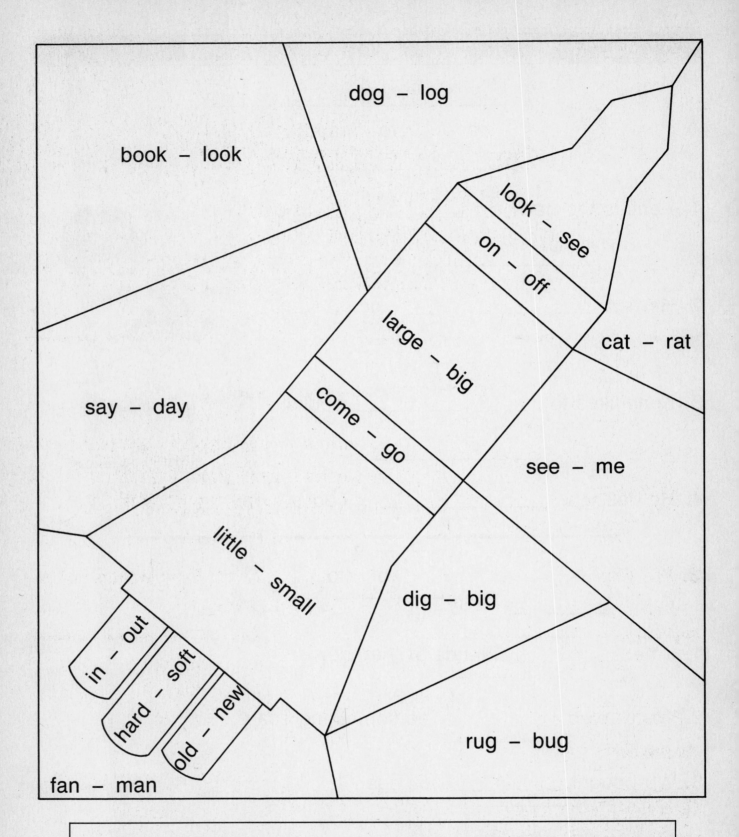

dog – log

book – look

look – see

on – off

large – big

cat – rat

say – day

come – go

see – me

little – small

dig – big

in – out

hard – soft

old – new

fan – man

rug – bug

Color **opposites** orange. Color **rhyming words** blue.

Color **words that mean the same** yellow.

Unit 2, Vocabulary. Read the color chart at the bottom of the page together with students. Help them read each pair of words, and tell them to fill in each space with the right color.

1. Pat sees the ball.

the ball

2. He gets it.

He gets

3. We like

We like the water.

4. The bird also likes water.

also likes water

5. I see her big truck.

her big truck

6. This is

This is my little truck.

Unit 3, Sentences. Have students look at each picture and read the groups of words under the picture. Then have them underline the group of words that is a sentence.

1. Max runs home.   Runs Max home.

----

2. Plays he ball.   He plays ball.

----

3. Mom late is.   Mom is late.

----

4. Comes here she.   Here she comes.

----

5. Mom plays, too.   Too plays Mom.

----

6. Fun they have.   They have fun.

----

7. Then they eat.   Eat then they.

----

8. Sleeps Max next.   Next, Max sleeps.

Unit 3, Sentences.   Have students read both groups of words in the first exercise. Ask which group makes sense. Then have students underline the group of words that makes sense, or is a sentence. Next have students rewrite the sentence on the lines below. Have students continue with the other exercises.

1. fast Jim swims

2. cannot swim I

3. math likes Pablo

4. Mike art likes

5. to town Eva walks

6. book a She gets

7. Kim bird sees a

8. red It is

Unit 3, Sentences. Have students write each sentence in correct word order. The sentence must make sense.

31

Sumi is **telling** her class about her trip.
This is what she said.

1. I went swimming.

2. I saw some animals.

3. I found a frog.

4. Dad took pictures.

5. We had a picnic.

6. It was fun.

7. I liked my trip.

Maria just met Carlos.
She is **asking** him questions.

1. What is your name?

_____

_____

2. When is your birthday?

_____

_____

3. Where do you live?

_____

_____

4. How old are you?

_____

_____

5. Who lives with you?

_____

_____

6. Did you meet my sister?

_____

_____

7. Why do you have a ball?

_____

_____

Unit 3, Sentences.   Have students copy each asking sentence.

1. I see a kite.

2. Is it for me?

3. We can fly the kite.

4. Will you race me?

5. Can you go fast?

6. Ben has my kite.

7. Is the sun hot?

Unit 3, Sentences.   Have students copy each sentence. Direct students to circle the number of each asking sentence and to put an *X* on the number of each telling sentence.

1. Rick went to the zoo.

_____

Who did something? _____

2. The monkey did some tricks.

_____

What did something? _____

3. The bear ate some food.

_____

What did something? _____

4. The lions roared.

_____

What did something? _____

5. The tiger slept in its cage.

_____

What did something? _____

6. Sue rode on an elephant.

_____

Who did something? _____

7. The pink birds ran together.

_____

What did something? _____

8. The turtle swam in the water.

_____

What did something? _____

Unit 3, Sentences.   Tell students that each sentence has a naming part that names someone or something. Have students read each sentence and the question below it; then have students write the answer to the question.

35

Sentence Parts That Show Action

1. Amy found a puppy.

_____

- -

What did Amy do? _____

2. The puppy ate some food.

_____

- -

What did the puppy do? _____

3. The puppy played with Amy.

_____

- -

What did the puppy do? _____

4. Amy named the puppy Skip.

_____

- -

What did Amy do? _____

5. Amy threw a ball.

_____

- -

What did Amy do? _____

6. Skip ran after the ball.

_____

- -

What did Skip do? _____

7. Skip got the ball.

_____

- -

What did Skip do? _____

8. Skip took a nap.

_____

- -

What did Skip do? _____

Unit 3, Sentences. Tell students that each sentence has an action part that shows what someone or something does. Have students read each sentence and the question below it; then have students write the answer to the question.

| ate the food. |
| fed the dogs. |
| helped Dan. |

1. Dan _____

_____

2. The dogs _____

_____

3. I _____

| The bird |
| Many friends |
| Pat |

1. _____ has a new bird.

2. _____ is very small.

3. _____ come to see it.

Unit 3, Sentences.   Have students read together the first naming part and each of the action parts; then have students write the action part that makes sense. Have students continue independently. At the bottom of the page, have students write the naming part that makes sense.

37

_____

1. Did you see the circus?

2. Yes, I saw the circus.

3. Was there a clown?

4. The clown was happy.

5. Was there a bear?

6. The bear did tricks.

7. Did you have fun?

8. We had fun.

The clown The bear The circus	was fun. was happy. did tricks.

1. _____

2. _____

3. _____

38 **Unit 3, Sentences.** Have students read the story at the top of the page and write *T* if the sentence is a telling sentence and *A* if it is an asking sentence. At the bottom of the page, have students match a naming part with an action part to make sentences. Have them write the sentence parts together.

dog	plays	and
ball	see	in
cat	has	with
hat	have	what
bird	is	where
tree	doing	a
duck	does	the

1. _____ .

2. _____ .

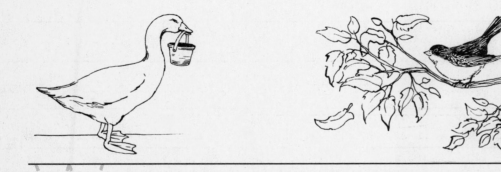

1. _____ ?

2. _____ ?

Unit 3, Sentences.   Have students look at the pictures. Have them write two telling sentences, then two asking sentences using some words in the box.

My school	reads books.
My teacher	likes me.
Our class	is fun.
My friend	is big.
Our playground	takes us places.
The bus	is happy.
Our room	looks nice.

My Story

1. _____

2. _____

3. _____

4. _____

5. _____

6. _____

7. _____

Unit 3, Sentences. Have students read the naming parts and the action parts in the boxes. Tell students to use these sentence parts to write a story about their school. Have students read their stories aloud to the class.

1. baby
man
girl

2. park
house
school

3. apple
car
fish

Unit 4, Grammar and Usage. Tell students that some words are naming words and that naming words can name people, places, or things. Then have students read each group of naming words and write the correct word under each picture.

41

1. The <u>boy</u> is ⟨Pat⟩
2. The <u>girl</u> is Mary.
3. The <u>baby</u> is Peg.
4. The <u>man</u> is Uncle Ted.
5. The <u>woman</u> is Aunt Ann.
6. My <u>sister</u> is Lee Chin.
7. My <u>brother</u> is Peter.

People	Special Names
1. *boy*	1. *Pat*
2.	2.
3.	3.
4.	4.
5.	5.
6.	6.
7.	7.

Unit 4, Grammar and Usage. Explain that people have special names. Have students read the underlined naming word in each sentence, then circle the special naming word. Have students write each naming word in the correct column. Remind students to use a capital letter to begin each special naming word.

My Story

1. The <u>city</u> I live in is (Kansas City).

2. The <u>street</u> I live on is First Street.

3. The <u>park</u> I play in is Peace Park.

4. The <u>beach</u> I swim at is Sun Beach.

5. My <u>library</u> is Elm Library.

6. The <u>store</u> I shop in is City Books.

Places	**Special Places**
1. _city_	1. _Kansas City_
2.	2.
3.	3.
4.	4.
5.	5.
6.	6.

Unit 4, Grammar and Usage.   Explain that many places have special names. Have students read the underlined naming word in each sentence, then circle the special naming word. Have students write each naming word in the correct column. Remind students to use a capital letter to begin each special naming word.

43

1. one bug

_____

three _____ bugs _____

3. one goat

_____

two _____

2. one dog

_____

four _____

4. one cat

_____

five _____

_____

1. I use my _____ to run.
(leg, legs)

2. I use my _____ to hear.
(ear, ears)

3. I use my _____ to see.
(eye, eyes)

4. I use my _____ to smell.
(nose, noses)

Unit 4, Grammar and Usage.   Have students look at the first picture and read *one bug.* Then have students read *three bugs* and trace *bugs.* Tell students to add *-s* to make the naming words in Exercises 2–4 mean more than one. Then have students read the remaining sentences and fill in the missing words.

eat	fly	ride	ring	run	swim

1. girls _____

2. birds _____

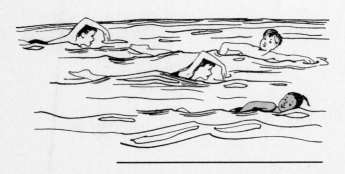

3. children _____

4. rabbits _____

5. puppies _____

6. bells _____

Unit 4, Grammar and Usage. Tell students that action words tell what people or things do. Have students choose a word from the box to tell what is happening in each picture, then write the word on the lines.

talk	goes	rides	sing

1. Our class _____ on a bus.

2. The bus _____ down the street.

3. We _____ songs.

4. We _____ to each other.

---

drop	eat	jump	walk

1. May I _____ the ice cream?

2. I will not _____ the cone.

3. I will _____ slowly with it.

4. I will not _____ up and down.

Unit 4, Grammar and Usage. Have students read the action words in the box at the top of the page. Then have them read each sentence, choose the word that makes sense, and write it on the lines. Follow the same procedure at the bottom of the page.

1. The boy play(s).

The boys play.

3. The toy works well.

The toys work well.

2. The dog jumps.

The dogs jump.

4. The ball rolls slowly.

The balls roll slowly.

---

1. The girl _____ rope.

The girls _____ rope.

2. The clocks _____ well.

The clock _____ well.

3. The orange _____ away.

The oranges _____ away.

4. My friends _____ with me.

My friend _____ with me.

Unit 4, Grammar and Usage.   Have students read the first set of sentences and discuss the differences in the action words. Have students underline the action words in sentences 2–4 and circle the *-s* on the action words. On the bottom of the page, have students write an underlined action word in each blank.

1. Today Lin _____ football.
(play, plays)

He _____ the ball far.
(kick, kicks)

2. Today Sue _____ to the park.
(walk, walks)

She _____ up the steps.
(climb, climbs)

3. Today Lupe _____ into the lake.
(jump, jumps)

She _____ in the water.
(walk, walks)

4. Today Ray _____ on the pond.
(skate, skates)

He _____ his friend skate.
(help, helps)

Unit 4, Grammar and Usage.   Tell students that *-s* is added to most action words to tell what one person or thing does today. Have students read each sentence and write the correct action word on the lines.

1. Yesterday Lin _____ football.
   (play, played)

He _____ the ball far.
   (kick, kicked)

2. Yesterday Sue _____ to the park.
   (walk, walked)

She _____ up the steps.
   (climb, climbed)

3. Yesterday Lupe _____ into the lake.
   (jump, jumped)

She _____ in the water.
   (walk, walked)

4. Last night Ray _____ on the pond.
   (skate, skated)

He _____ his friend skate.
   (help, helped)

Unit 4, Grammar and Usage.   Tell students that *-ed* is added to most action words to tell what happened
in the past. Have students read each sentence and write the correct action word on the lines.

49

_____ _____

__is__ or __are__

_____

1. He _____ my father.

_____

2. She _____ my mother.

_____

3. Father and Mother _____ in the garden.

_____

4. Sue and I _____ in the garden, too.

_____

5. The flowers _____ pretty.

_____

6. Sue _____ four years old.

_____

7. Our dogs _____ in the yard.

_____

8. One dog _____ black and white.

_____

9. Both dogs _____ little.

Unit 4, Grammar and Usage. Tell students to use *is* when they speak of one person or thing in the present and to use *are* when they speak of more than one person or thing in the present. Have students read each sentence and write *is* or *are* on the lines.

_____   _____
------**was**------ or ------**were**------

_____
----
1. I _____ at the park.

_____
----
2. My dog _____ at the park.

_____
----
3. We _____ at the park together.

_____
----
4. My friend _____ there, too.

_____
----
5. We _____ at the park to play ball.

_____
----
6. The bats _____ brown.

_____
----
7. The balls _____ white.

_____
----
8. The game _____ fun.

_____
----
9. It _____ a great day!

Unit 4, Grammar and Usage.   Tell students to use *was* when they speak of one person or thing in the past and to use *were* when they speak of more than one person or thing in the past. Have students read each sentence and write *was* or *were* on the lines.

51

1. I (see, saw) a red balloon now.

2. Yesterday Ann (see, saw) a blue balloon.

3. Now Kim and Ann (see, saw) a green balloon.

4. Last night Kim (ran, run) to the store.

5. Now I (ran, run) to the store.

6. Yesterday Ann (ran, run) home from school.

7. Now Kim and Ann (ran, run) to the park.

8. Now I (come, came) to the park.

9. Yesterday Kim and Ann (come, came) to my house.

10. Now they (come, came) again.

---

1. I __ (see, saw) a pretty picture now.

2. Last night Kim __ (ran, run) fast.

3. Then she __ (come, came) to see me.

4. I __ (see, saw) another friend yesterday.

Unit 4, Grammar and Usage. Tell students to use *see, come,* and *run* to tell something that happens today and to use *saw, came,* and *ran* to tell something that happened in the past. Have students circle the correct word in the first ten sentences, then rewrite the next four sentences correctly.

Jan reads.
She reads.

Bob writes.
He writes.

1. Jan has a rabbit.

She

2. Bob has a fish.

3. Jan pets the rabbit.

4. Bob feeds the fish.

5. Jan eats lunch.

6. Bob eats lunch, too.

Unit 4, Grammar and Usage.   Have students read the sentences at the top of the page and note which words are used in place of the names. Then have students read the first sentence aloud and substitute the word *she* for the name. Have students rewrite the sentences, making each one begin with *He* or *She.*

53

Tom and I will play.
We will play.

Lee, Pat, and Bill will play.
They will play.

1. Tom and I are here.

2. Lee, Pat, and Bill are not here.

3. Lee, Pat, and Bill are late.

4. Tom and I will play.

5. Tom and I can win.

6. Lee, Pat, and Bill will not play.

Unit 4, Grammar and Usage. Have students read the sentences at the top of the page and note which words are used in place of the names. Read the first sentence together, and have students substitute the word *we* for the names. Have students rewrite the sentences, making each one begin with *We* or *They*.

| I see you. | Mom and I see you. |

1. Jim and ___ go to the park.

_____

_____

2. Jim and ___ fish.

_____

_____

3. ___ sit on the grass.

_____

_____

4. ___ sit by Jim.

_____

_____

5. ___ help Jim.

_____

_____

6. Jim and ___ catch fish.

_____

_____

7. ___ look at the water.

_____

_____

8. Jim and ___ have fun.

_____

_____

Unit 4, Grammar and Usage.   Have students read the two examples of the proper use of _I_. Then have students add _I_ to each sentence and rewrite the sentence on the lines.

a b c d e f g h i j k l m

n o p q r s t u v w x y z

—— —— —— —— ——
1. The vowels are ____, ____, ____, ____, ____.

2. _____ apple

4. _____ egg

3. _____ insect

5. _____ orange

---

1. _____ ice cream cone

4. _____ toy truck

2. _____ baby bottle

5. _____ oak tree

3. _____ animal shop

6. _____ barnyard

Unit 4, Grammar and Usage.   Have students say the alphabet and write the shaded letters called vowels. Tell students that *an* is used before words that begin with a vowel. Then have students read each word, circle the first vowel, and write *an*. Next have students write *an* only in front of the appropriate phrases.

abcdefghijklm
nopqrstuvwxyz

_____
- - - - - - - -
1. _____ train
(a, an)

_____
- - - - - - - -
2. _____ tent
(a, an)

_____
- - - - - - - -
3. _____ bug
(a, an)

_____
- - - - - - - -
4. _____ bike
(a, an)

_____
- - - - - - - -
5. _____ van
(a, an)

_____
- - - - - - - -
6. _____ uncle
(a, an)

_____
- - - - - - - -
7. _____ ant
(a, an)

_____
- - - - - - - -
8. _____ ship
(a, an)

1. I saw _____.

2. I can ride on _____.

Unit 4, Grammar and Usage.   Have students say the alphabet and circle the consonants. Tell them that
a is used before words that begin with a consonant. Have students read each word and write *a* or *an* on
the lines. At the bottom of the page, have students complete the sentences using phrases from the page.

1.

hot

sad

cold

3.

muddy

good

clean

2.

sad

happy

mad

4.

cold

hot

long

1. Ice cream is _cold_.

2. Gina looks _____.

3. The boots are _____.

4. The pan is _____.

Unit 4, Grammar and Usage. Have students identify the pictures and read the words together. Have students circle one word in each box that tells how the thing or person looks or feels. Then have students write the correct circled word in each sentence at the bottom of the page.

1. Sally likes her big old cat.
It is gray and white and so soft.

Which words tell about Sally's cat?

red   white   old   big

gray   pretty   soft   wet

2. A little duck walked in the yard.
The duck was white and black.

Which words tell about the duck?

sad   white   dark   black

bad   little   lost   big

3. Joe lost his old brown cap.
Then he got a new red cap.

Which words tell about Joe's new cap?

old   brown   blue   lost

new   clean   red   tall

Unit 4, Grammar and Usage.   Have students read each story together. Then have them circle the words that answer each question.

1. Aunt Liz drove the young children to the circus.

2. The large elephants walked into a brown tent.

3. The funny clown kicked his big feet.

4. The happy children clapped their hands.

---

1. We _____ in school.
(is, are)

2. My mom _____ here.
(is, are)

3. Do you _____ those books?
(see, saw)

4. The books _____ big.
(was, were)

---

1. John   she

2. Sue   he

3. Sue and John   we

4. Bill and I   they

Unit 4, Grammar and Usage. Have students listen carefully to your directions (which appear in the *Teacher's Guide*).

1. Ted and Eva _____ in the park.
(is, are)

2. Ted _____ fast.
(walk, walks)

3. Eva _____ slowly.
(walk, walks)

4. Ted and Eva _____ in the yard yesterday.
(play, played)

5. Ted _____ a ball.
(kick, kicked)

6. Eva _____ .
(skate, skated)

| He | She | They |

1. _____

2. _____

3. _____

4. _____

The Farm

1. The farm _____ big.
(is, are)

It is _____ big farm.
(a, an)

2. The farmer has _____ cow.
(a, an)

It is _____ old cow.
(a, an)

3. Many animals _____ on the farm.
(is, are)

The animals _____ and play.
(run, runs)

4. One cat _____ inside.
(play, plays)

Two _____ play outside.
(cat, cats)

Unit 4, Grammar and Usage. Have students read each sentence, select the correct word, and write it on the lines.

1. A dog is a good pet.

2. My dog can run fast.

3. Rags can play ball.

4. Rags can jump.

5. Do you want a pet?

6. I will give you a pup.

---

1. the sun is hot.
_____
- -
_____

2. we will go home.
_____
- -
_____

3. you can come with us.
_____
- -
_____

4. we will get some water.
_____
- -
_____

Jesse   Aunt Ann

_____   _____
- - - - - - - - - - - - - -   - - - - - - - - - - - - - -
1. _____   2. _____

_____

_____
- -
1. pat long   _____

_____
- -
2. eva ramos   _____

_____
- -
3. uncle bill   _____

_____
- -
4. will brown   _____

Unit 5, Capitalization and Punctuation. Tell students that names of people always begin with a capital letter. Have students underline the capital letters that begin the first two names, then rewrite them. Have students rewrite the names at the bottom of the page, beginning each with a capital letter.

| chip | muff | king | jet | goldy | speedy |

1. _____

4. _____

2. _____

5. _____

3. _____

6. _____

Unit 5, Capitalization and Punctuation. Tell students that names for animals also begin with capital letters. Have students name each pet, using the words in the box. Then have students rewrite each name with a capital letter.

1. What day comes before Tuesday?

_____

- -

_____

2. What day comes after Thursday?

_____

- -

_____

Sunday
Monday
Tuesday
Wednesday
Thursday
Friday
Saturday

3. What day comes before Monday?

_____

- -

_____

4. What two days start with the letter T?

_____   _____

- - - - - - - - - - - - - - - -   - - - - - - - - - - - - - - - -

_____   _____

5. What two days start with the letter S?

_____   _____

- - - - - - - - - - - - - - - -   - - - - - - - - - - - - - - - -

_____   _____

6. What are the last two days of the week?

_____   _____

- - - - - - - - - - - - - - - -   - - - - - - - - - - - - - - - -

_____   _____

7. What day begins with W?

_____

- -

_____

Unit 5, Capitalization and Punctuation. Tell students that the name of each day begins with a capital letter. Have students read the list of days. Discuss the meanings of the words *before, after,* and *last.* Then have students answer the questions.

1. january

_____

- -

_____

2. february

_____

- -

_____

3. march

_____

- -

_____

4. april

_____

- -

_____

5. may

_____

- -

_____

6. june

_____

- -

_____

7. july

_____

- -

_____

8. august

_____

- -

_____

9. september

_____

- -

_____

10. october

_____

- -

_____

11. november

_____

- -

_____

12. december

_____

- -

_____

Unit 5, Capitalization and Punctuation. Tell students that the name of each month begins with a capital letter. Have students read the names of the months. Then have students rewrite the names, capitalizing each one.

1. Bo lives on jones street.

_____

- -

_____.

2. He works on river road.

_____

- -

_____.

3. I live on oak street.

_____

- -

_____.

4. I work on lake drive.

_____

- -

_____.

1. Diane lives in dallas.

_____

- -

_____.

2. She came from new york.

_____

- -

_____.

3. My home is in chicago.

_____

- -

_____.

4. My friend lives in boston.

_____

- -

_____.

Unit 5, Capitalization and Punctuation. Tell students that names of places, such as cities and streets, begin with a capital letter. Have students read the first four sentences, underline the street names, and rewrite the sentences using capital letters where needed. Repeat the procedure with city names.

I am a boy.

I am a girl.

I am at home.

I am not at home.

I have a pet.

I feed my pet.

My friend and I like to swim.

My friend and I like to read.

My friend and I run each day.

My friend and I go to school.

My friend and I play ball.

My friend and I play games.

1. _____

2. _____

3. _____

4. _____

5. _____

6. _____

7. _____

Unit 5, Capitalization and Punctuation. Tell students that the word *I* is always written with a capital letter. Have students read the sentences at the top of the page. Then have students choose seven of the sentences to write a story about themselves.

69

1. Bob has a book ▨

2. The book is old ▨

3. Bob likes his book ▨

4. It is a good book ▨

5. I want to read it ▨

6. It is about bugs ▨

_____

1. This is my home

----

2. I cut the grass

----

3. Next, I rake it

----

4. It looks good

Unit 5, Capitalization and Punctuation. Tell students that telling sentences always end with a period. Have students read each telling sentence at the top of the page and put a period at the end. Then have students rewrite each sentence at the bottom of the page correctly.

1. Who is here

2. When will it be time to go

3. Will we go soon

4. Do you have your coat

5. Where is my coat

6. Who is going with us

---

1. Who said my name

_____

- - - - - - - - - - - - - - - - - -

_____

2. Was it Bud

_____

- - - - - - - - - - - - - - - - - -

_____

3. Did Bud go home

_____

- - - - - - - - - - - - - - - - - -

_____

4. When will he come back

_____

- - - - - - - - - - - - - - - - - -

_____

Unit 5, Capitalization and Punctuation.   Tell students that asking sentences end with a question mark. Have students read each asking sentence at the top of the page and put a question mark at the end. Then have students rewrite each sentence at the bottom of the page correctly.

. or **?**

1. It will rain all day

2. Where can we have a picnic

3. We can have it on the porch

4. You and I will make the food

5. What food do you like

6. I like hot dogs

7. Who will get the chairs

8. Who will sit next to me

9. Tom will sit next to me

10. We will play games

11. Who will win

12. When will the sun shine

Unit 5, Capitalization and Punctuation. Have students read the sentences. Tell students to put a period at the end of each telling sentence and a question mark at the end of each asking sentence.

January 1, 1989   July 4, 1987

1. I got a Valentine on february 14 1989.

_____

- -

_____

2. Jan had a New Year's party on january 1 1988.

_____

- -

_____

3. I dressed up like a pumpkin on october 31 1986.

_____

- -

_____

4. Leo ate turkey on november 23 1988.

_____

- -

_____

5. My Fourth of July party was on july 4 1988.

_____

- -

_____

6. Greg left for his summer vacation on august 9 1989.

_____

- -

_____

7. Today is ___.

_____

- -

_____

Unit 5, Capitalization and Punctuation.   Tell students that a comma means to pause, then read on. Have students read the dates in the box. Point out the capital letters. Tell them a comma is used to separate the day from the year. Have students circle each date, then write each date correctly.

1. joe garza and i walk to school

2. we will shop on friday

3. did joe call uncle ray

4. last friday i called ray

5. do you work on monday

6. i work on monday

---

1. i saw aunt sue

_____

- -

_____

2. she lives on lee road

_____

- -

_____

3. she was born may 1 1968

_____

- -

_____

4. her dog is named wags

_____

- -

_____

Unit 5, Capitalization and Punctuation. Have students read the sentences at the top of the page and circle each word that should have a capital letter. Then have them put the correct punctuation at the end of each sentence. Have students rewrite each sentence correctly at the bottom of the page.

1. My name is ___.

2. My street is ___.

3. My city is ___.

4. My school is ___.

5. The street my school is on is ___.

6. My birthday is ___.

7. Today's date is ___.

8. The day of the week is ___.

Unit 5, Capitalization and Punctuation. Have students write the information that completes each sentence. Remind students to use capital letters and commas where needed.

75

1. where is bill
2. he is in the house
3. bill has two cookies
4. what is bill doing
5. he is making a snack

6. can he cook
7. what is he making
8. the snack is sweet
9. it is a good snack
10. would you like some

1. _____

2. _____

3. _____

4. _____

5. _____

6. _____

7. _____

8. _____

9. _____

10. _____

Unit 5, Capitalization and Punctuation. Have students read each sentence at the top of the page. Have them rewrite the sentences on the lines, using capital letters and punctuation where needed.

| flowers | friend | garden | rain | seeds | store | sun | table |

_____

1. Jo went to the _____.

_____

2. She got some little brown _____.

_____

3. Jo will plant the seeds in the _____.

_____

4. The _____ will fall on the garden.

_____

5. The _____ will warm the garden.

_____

6. Pretty _____ will grow in the garden.

_____

7. Jo will give the flowers to a _____.

_____

8. Her friend will put them on a _____.

Unit 6, Composition. Have students choose naming words from the box to complete each sentence.

| bark | climbs | chase | eat | jump | plays | run | sleeps |

1. The two dogs _____ fast.

2. The dogs _____ up.

3. They _____ their food.

4. The dogs _____ the cat.

5. The dogs _____ loudly.

6. The cat _____ a tree.

7. Then one dog _____ with a ball.

8. The other dog _____ under a tree.

Unit 6, Composition.   Have students choose action words from the box to complete each sentence.

78

Are you sleeping or resting?

I am resting.

1. Are you a boy or a girl?

_____

- -

_____

2. Are you sitting or standing?

_____

- -

_____

3. Do you use a pen or a pencil?

_____

- -

_____

4. Do you walk or ride to school?

_____

- -

_____

5. Do you like grapes or plums?

- -

_____

6. Is it day or night now?

_____

- -

_____

7. Is it cold or hot today?

_____

- -

_____

Unit 6, Composition.   Discuss the example with students. Then have students read the questions and
write each answer as a complete sentence.

Naming	Action
The birds	runs.
That frog	digs.
The fish	swim.
A deer	fly.
My dog	hops.

(Line drawn connecting "The birds" to "fly.")

1. The _____
Naming   Action

_____

2. _____
Naming   Action

_____

3. _____
Naming   Action

_____

4. _____
Naming   Action

_____

5. _____
Naming   Action

Unit 6, Composition. Have students draw lines to match the sentence parts. Then have them write the sentences on the lines below.

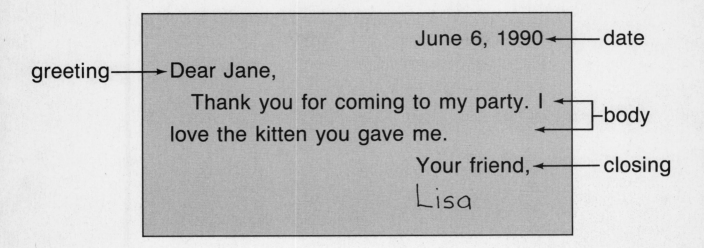

June 6, 1990 ← date

greeting → Dear Jane,

    Thank you for coming to my party. I ← body
love the kitten you gave me.

      Your friend, ← closing

      Lisa

1. Dear Jane,

2. Dear Mother,

3. Dear Tom,

1. Your friend,

_____
(your name)

2. Love,

Father

Unit 6, Composition. Read and discuss the parts of the letter. Then have students rewrite the greetings and closings. Remind them to use commas as shown.

81

May 1, 19 _____

Dear Zookeeper,
   Thank you for the book you sent our class. It was a very good animal story.
           Yours truly,

       Grade One

Dear _____

Unit 6, Composition. Have students read the thank-you letter, insert the correct year in the date, and write the letter on the lines.

I have a new red bike.
It is something that I like.
I ride and ride my bike around.
And blow the horn to hear the sound.

Dad and I went to the park.

We had to be home before it was ___.

(light, Monday, dark)

We sat on a swing and went up high.

I thought that we would touch the ___.

(clouds, sky, ground)

Bob and Sue like to cook.

They do what it says in the ___.

(mail, book, show)

Bob will get the box of fish.

Sue will put it in the ___.

(box, dish, pot)

Unit 6, Composition. Remind students that some words rhyme. Read the first poem together, and have students circle the rhyming words. Then have students read the other poems and circle the correct rhyming word.

letters	mouse	plays	write

1. Do you like to get _____?

2. Let's _____ a letter.

3. We can tell about our pet _____.

4. It _____ in its cage.

A. Body	B. Closing	C. Date	D. Greeting

May 7, 1990   **1.** ____

2. ____ Dear Uncle Kevin,

____   Thank you for taking me to the circus.

3. ____ I had a good time.

Love,   ____

Kendra   **4.** ____

Unit 6, Composition.   Have students choose a word from the box to complete each sentence at the top of the page. Then have students label the parts of the letter.

children	bell	girls
friends	boys	ball

rings	rolls	walk
play	talk	run

1. The _____ _____ at three o'clock.

2. The _____ _____ out the door.

3. Three _____ _____ home.

4. Two _____ _____ about school.

5. Four _____ _____ ball.

6. The _____ _____ into a garden.

7. Write your own sentence.
_____

_____

Unit 6, Composition. Have students complete each sentence using a word from the box on the left in the first blank and a word from the box on the right in the second blank.

85

1. May 5, 19___
2. Dear Pat,
3. Thank you for letting me visit your class.
   I had a nice time.
4. Your friend,
   Dr. Turner

Unit 6, Composition.   Read the parts of the letter together. Have students write the letter on the lines, using the current year.

Finding the Ones That Are Alike

1.

2.

3.

ABC Order

1. rain
   girl
   car

3. Juan
   Diane
   Maria

2. truck
   water
   zoo

4. house
   man
   fly

Readiness/Study Skills.   At the top of the page, have students circle the things in each row that are alike.
Then have students write the words at the bottom of the page in alphabetical order.

87

Rhyming Words

1. The cat sat on the mat.

2. A bug is on the rug.

3. The frog will hop on the mop.

4. The brown bear ate a pear.

5. A bee is in the tree.

6. I have fun when I run in the sun.

7. Jim took a ride down the slide.

8. Sue saw her coat on the boat.

9. Pat likes to skate by the gate.

10. Is there a mouse in Pat's house?

Like Words

1. dark   large   big

2. go   leave   come

3. print   sing   write

4. high   short   tall

5. end   start   begin

6. small   old   little

Opposite Words

1. Please close the door. (shut, open)

2. It is very hot outside. (cold, warm)

3. I think we should play inside. (work, stay)

Vocabulary. At the top of the page, have students read each sentence and circle the rhyming words. In the middle of the page, have students circle the words that mean almost the same. At the bottom of the page, have students circle the word that means the opposite of the underlined word.

Asking and Telling Sentences

1. _____ Does Juan like animals?

2. _____ Juan likes animals.

3. _____ He feeds the

4. _____ Juan will give milk to the cat.

5. _____ Do you have a pet?

Making Sentences

The sun	went for a walk.
The sky	was shining.
I	went with me.
My friend	was blue.

1. _____

2. _____

3. _____

4. _____

Sentences.   At the top of the page, have students underline each group of words that is a sentence and write *T* if the sentence is a telling sentence or *A* if it is an asking sentence. At the bottom of the page, have students draw lines to match a naming part with an action part to make sentences. Have them write the sentences.

Naming Words and Action Words

1. Dad walked to the store.

2. Mom rode the bus to Elm City.

3. John plays in the park.

4. Lee jumped rope.

Using <u>Is/Are</u> and <u>Was/Were</u>

1. My dog (is, are) funny.

2. The girls (is, are) laughing.

3. My dog (was, were) running.

4. The boys (was, were) running, too.

5. Pat (was, were) jumping.

6. We (was, were) having fun!

Using <u>A</u> or <u>An</u>

1. _____ boat

2. _____ apple

3. _____ bus

4. _____ egg

5. _____ door

6. _____ uncle

Grammar and Usage. Have students underline the naming words and circle the action words in the first set of sentences. Then have students underline the correct word in the second set of sentences. Finally, have students write *a* or *an* as needed.

Writing Sentences Correctly

1. ray worked with tony

_____

- -

_____

2. did they work on monday

_____

- -

_____

3. yes, they worked for uncle ed

_____

- -

_____

4. i saw them in july

_____

- -

_____

5. do they live in chicago

_____

- -

_____

6. jim and i were born in may

_____

- -

_____

7. i met jim in new york

_____

- -

_____

8. aunt liz will visit in april

_____

- -

_____

Capitalization and Punctuation. Have students rewrite the sentences correctly using capital letters, periods, and question marks.

Writing Sentences

1. How old are you?

_____
- -
_____

2. Do you like to read or write?

_____
- -
_____

3. Are you at school or at home?

_____
- -
_____

Writing a Letter

_____
- -
1. _____

_____
- -
2. _____

Thank you for taking us to the zoo. We had fun.
We liked the bears and the monkeys.

_____
- -
3. _____

_____
- -
4. _____

| Dear Uncle Ed, | July 9, 1990 |
| Bob and Meg | Love, |

92

Composition. Have students answer the questions at the top of the page with complete sentences. Then have students write the parts of the letter on the correct lines.